Beauty is in the eyes of the beholder

Inspiring book

Wendy Rothery

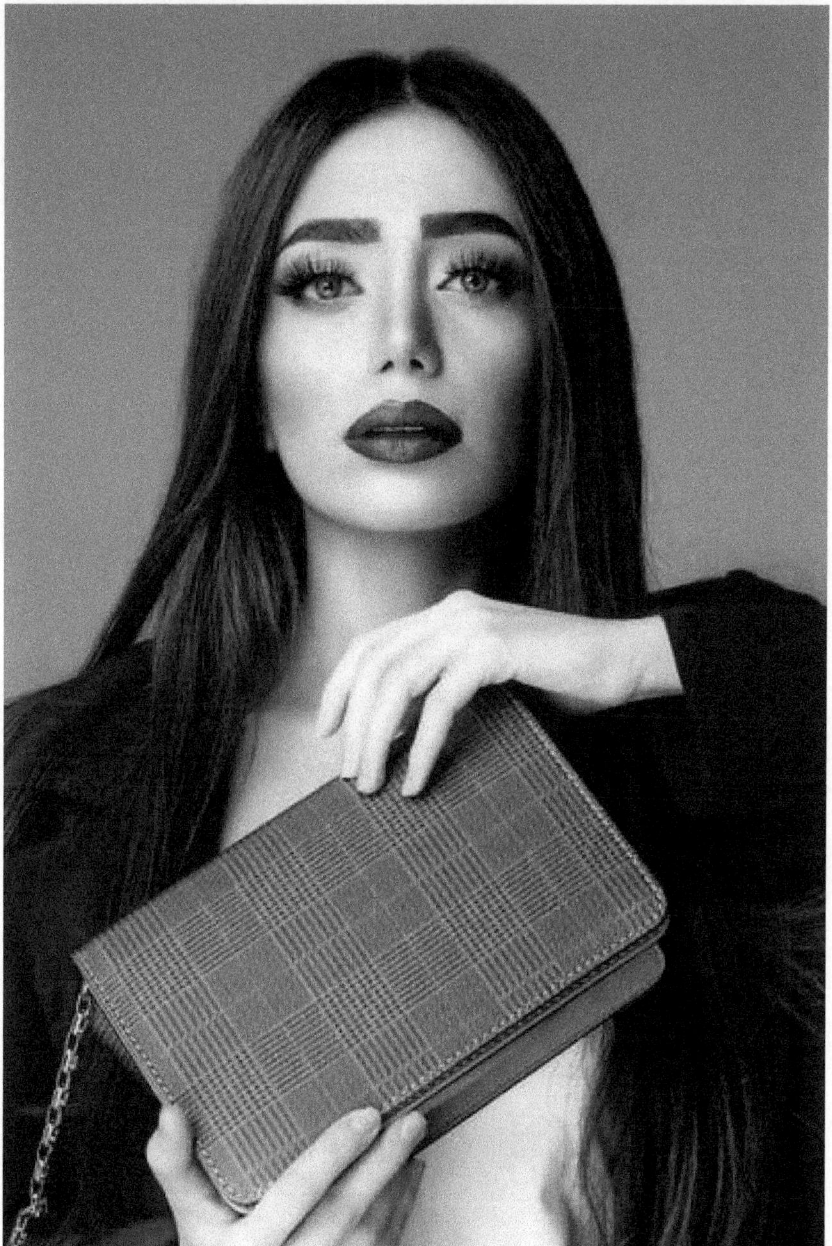

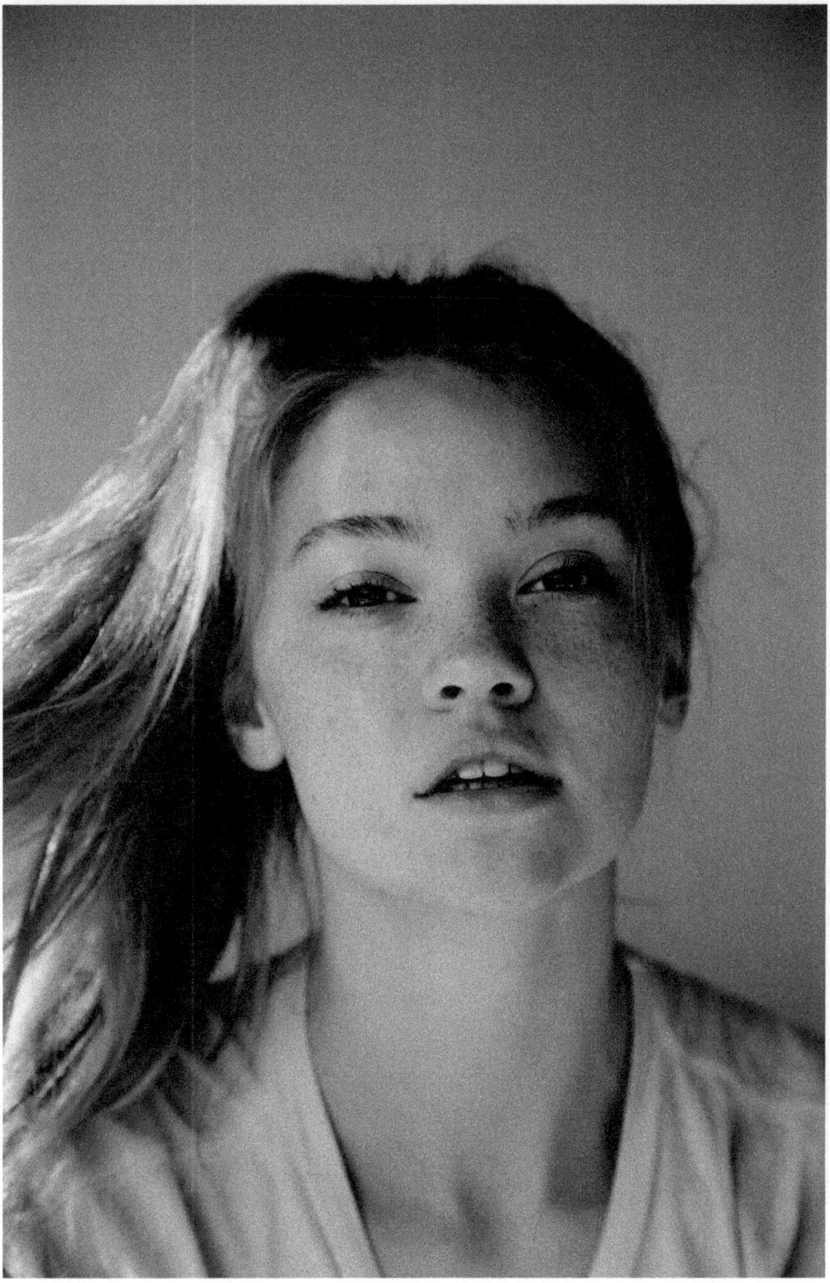

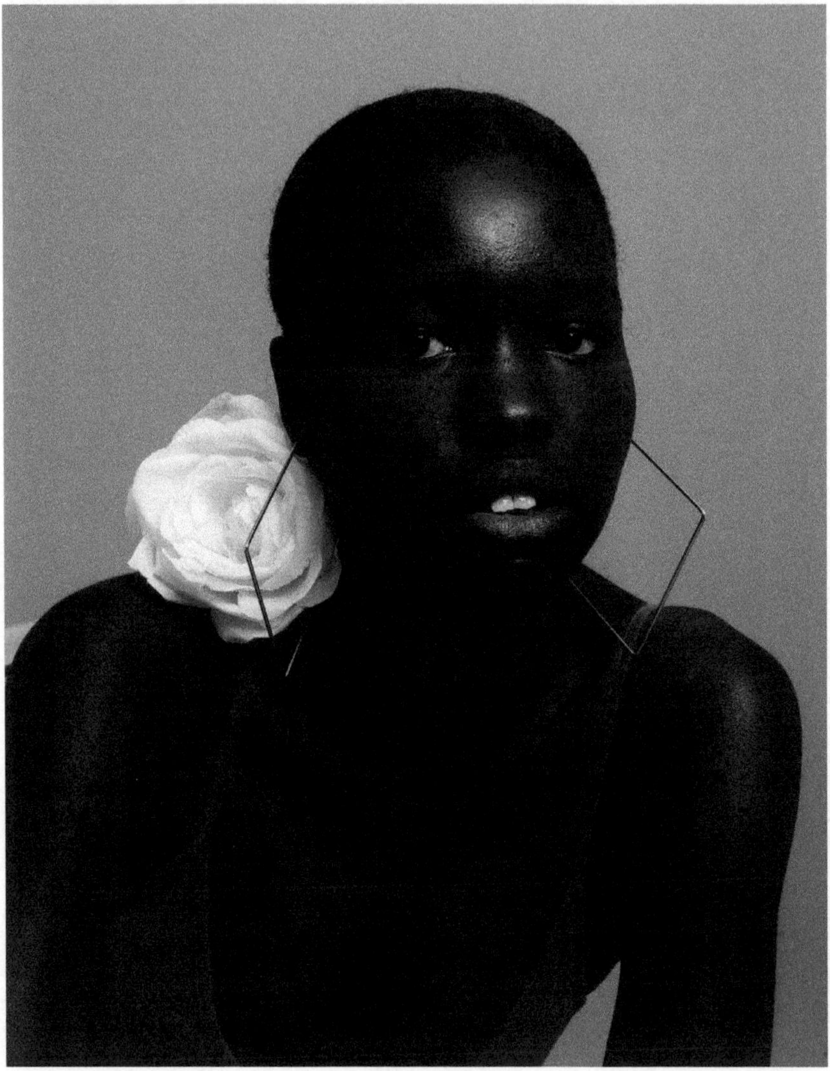

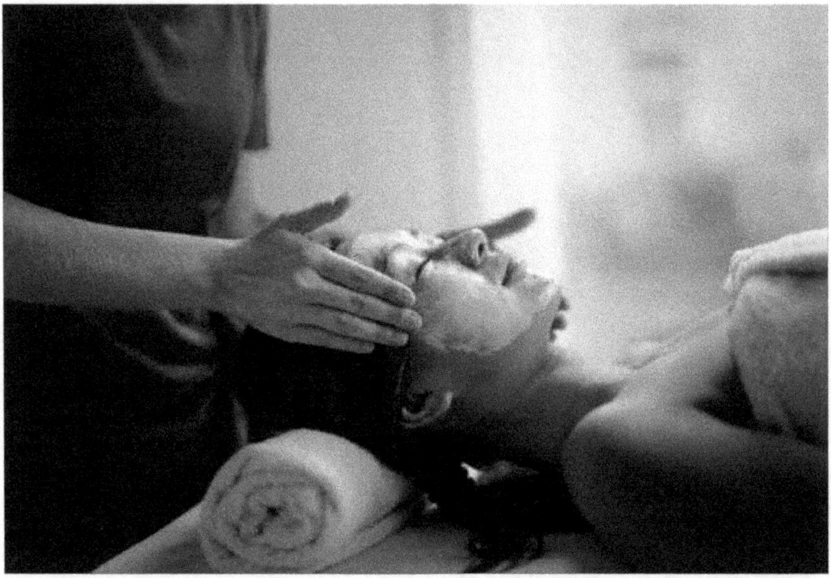

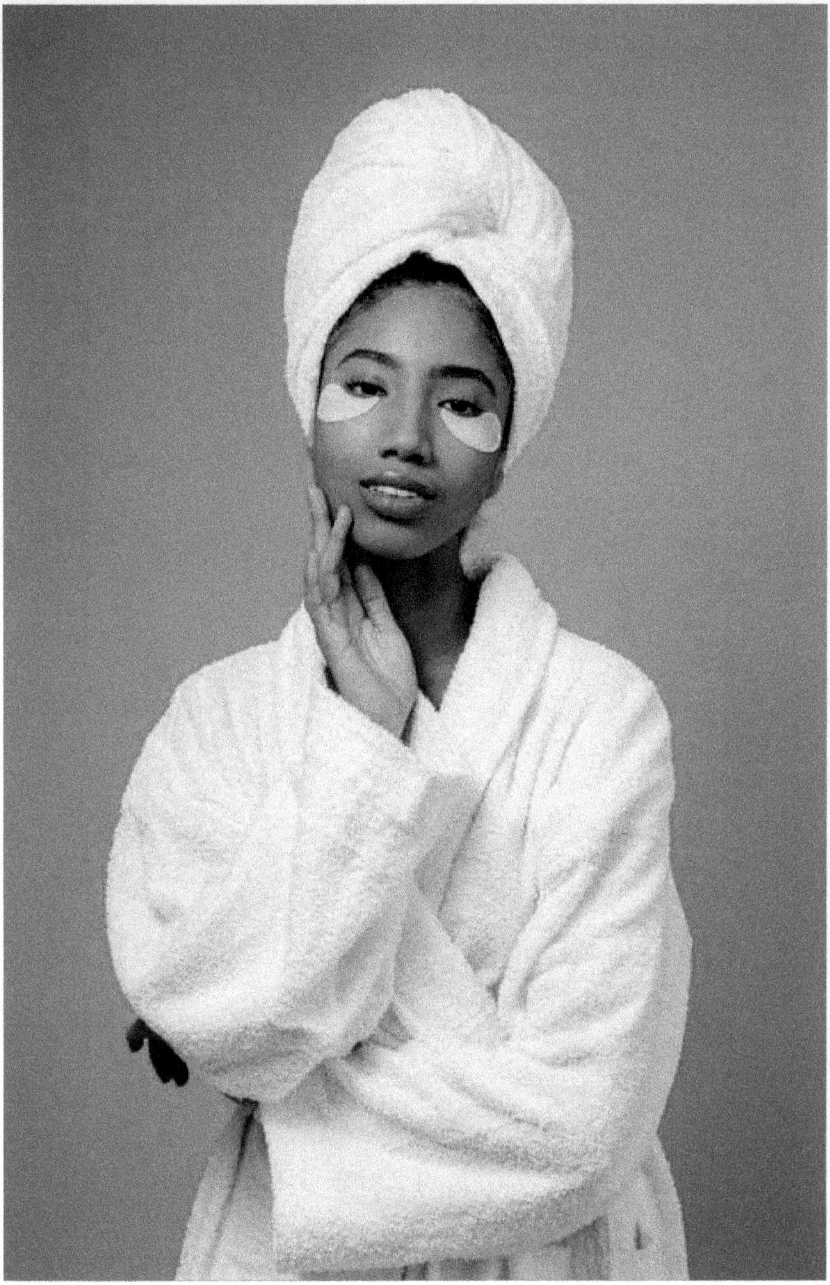

PERIGO
BRIGO DE GAS
BLOCO 6
ÃO FUME

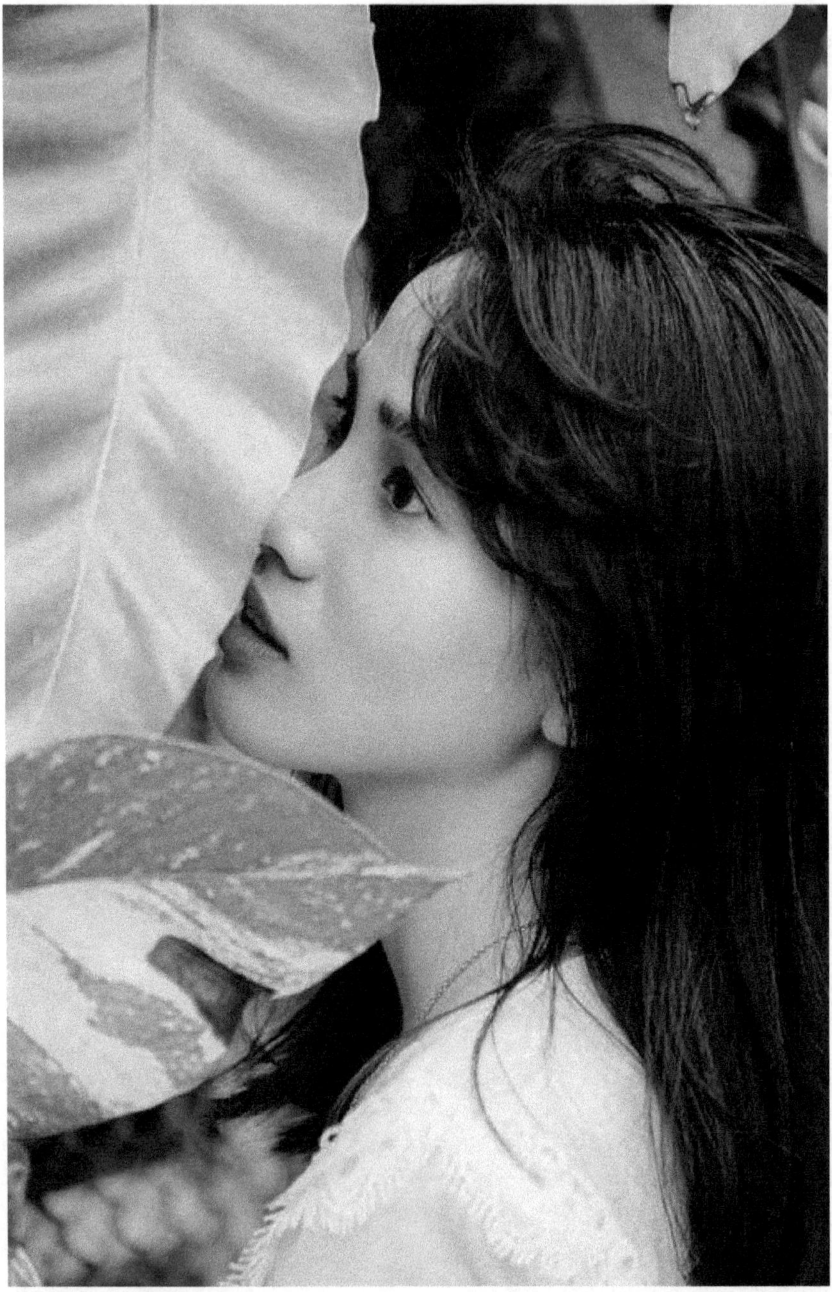

Lightning Source UK Ltd.
Milton Keynes UK
UKHW020742250621
386134UK00001B/56

9 781803 101378